Testing and assessment in the National Curriculum

Pupils between the ages of 7 and 11 (Years 3–6) cover Key Stage 2 of the National Curriculum. In May of their final year of Key Stage 2 (Year 6) all pupils take written National Tests (commonly known as SATs) in the three most important subjects: English, Mathematics and Science. Your child may already have taken some National Tests at the end of Key Stage 1 (Year 2). These will have been in number, shape and space, reading, writing, handwriting and spelling.

At the end of Key Stage 1, your child will have been awarded a National Curriculum level for each subject tested. When your child eventually takes the Key Stage 2 tests, he or she again will be awarded a level. On average, pupils are expected to advance one level for every two years they are at school. The target for pupils at the end of Key Stage 1 is Level 2. By the end of Key Stage 2, four years later, the target is Level 4. The table below will show you how your child should progress.

		7 years	11 years
▨ Exceptional performance	Level 6		▨
	Level 5		▨
▨ Exceeded targets for age group	Level 4	▨	☐
☐ Achieved targets for age group	Level 3	▨	☐
	Level 2	☐	☐
☐ Working towards targets for age group	Level 1	☐	☐

Assessing your child's progress throughout Key Stage 2 of the National Curriculum

The aim of the Letts Assessment books is to help you monitor your child's progress in English, Mathematics and Science throughout Key Stage 2. There are four books for each subject – one for each year, starting with 7–8 year olds. The questions in the books become progressively harder with each year, so that for 10–11 year olds, the questions will be at a level similar to the Key Stage 2 National Tests.

After completing a book, your child will have a score which you will be able to interpret using the progress indicator provided. This will give you a guide to the level at which your child is working.

Using this book to assess your child's progress in Science

This book is for 10–11 year olds (Year 6). It contains four basic features:

Questions:	33 questions, arranged in order of difficulty as follows: 8 at Level 3 (pages 1–7) 11 at Level 4 (pages 8–19) 3 at Level 4/5 (pages 20–22) 11 at Level 5 (pages 23–36)
Answers:	showing acceptable responses and marks
Note to Parent:	giving advice on what your child should be doing and how to help
Progress Chart:	showing you how to interpret your child's marks to arrive at a level

- Your child should not attempt to do all the questions in the book in one go. Try setting ten questions at a time. If your child does not understand a question, you might want to explain it. Although the questions in this book are not meant to constitute a formal test, you should encourage your child to answer as many as possible without help. Read the questions to your child if you think it will help.

- When your child has completed the questions, turn to the Answer section at the back of the book. Using the recommended answers, award your child the appropriate mark or marks for each question. In the margin of each question page, there are small boxes. These are divided in half with the marks available for that question at the bottom, and a blank at the top for you to fill in your child's score.

- Collate your child's marks on the grid on page 46. Then add them up. Once you have the total, turn to page 37 at the front of the Answer section and look at the Progress Chart to determine your child's level.

- Work through the answers with your child, using the Note to Parent to help give advice, correct mistakes and explain problems.

Equipment your child will need for this book

All your child needs are a pen or pencil for writing, and a pencil for drawing. Your child may also like to have a rubber for changing answers. Where lines have to be drawn, they can be drawn either with a ruler or freehand, whichever your child feels most comfortable with.

1 | Draw lines to match up each material with its property and use. |

| **Material** | **Use** | **Property** |

| glass | raft | hard |

| iron | windows | transparent |

| silver | nails | floats on water |

| wood | medals | shiny |

2 David uses a piece of wood, two nails and an elastic band to make a musical instrument.

a | What does David have to do to play the instrument? |

....

b | How can David make the sound louder? |

....

3   In your body you have over
200 bones.

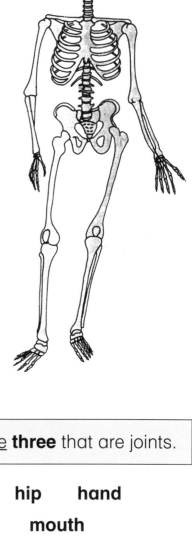

1

Q3a

a
What job do bones do?

....

....

1

Q3b

b
What job do muscles do?

....

....

You have lots of joints in your body.

1

Q3c

c
On the picture, label **two** of them
with the letter **J**.

3

Q3d

d
Look at this list of body parts. <u>Underline</u> **three** that are joints.

head   knee   chest   hip   hand

arm   elbow   foot   mouth

1

Q3e

e
Why do jellyfish not need bones?

....

....

4   Here are some bulbs connected to some batteries.

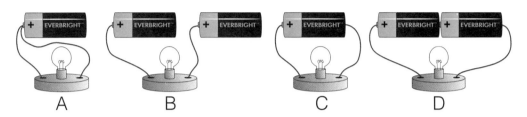

A   B   C   D

Tick ✓ the correct box for each bulb.

Bulb	Lights	Does not light
A		
B		
C		
D		

4

Q4

5   Ice can be melted and then turned back into ice by freezing.

a   What must you do to ice to melt it?

1

Q5a

b   Here are some more changes. Tick ✓ **three** boxes to show changes that can also be reversed.

3

Q5b

baking bread   ☐   melting wax   ☐

bending plasticine   ☐   cutting paper   ☐

burning coal   ☐   drying a towel   ☐

3

6   Look at these pictures of people parachuting.

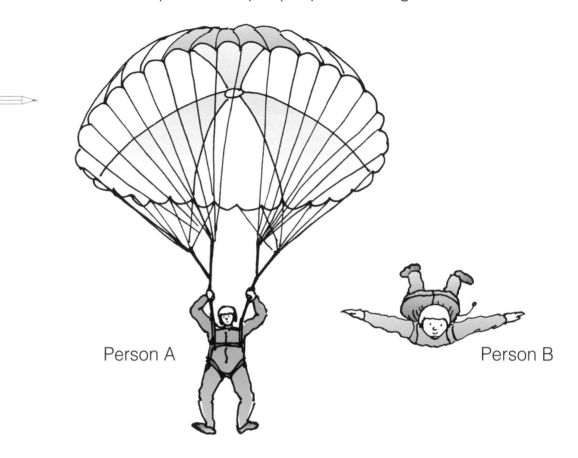

Person A   Person B

a

| Which person will fall faster through the air? |

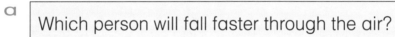 Person ....

b

| What force makes these people fall? |

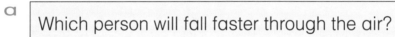 ....

c

| Draw an arrow on **B** to show the force which makes her fall. |

d

| Draw an arrow on **A** to show the force which slows him down when he opens the parachute. |

1

Q6a

1

Q6b

1

Q6c

1

Q6d

4

7   Birds do not have teeth so they cannot chew food. They swallow food whole and then grind it up in their stomachs. The size and shape of a bird's beak depends on the food it eats.

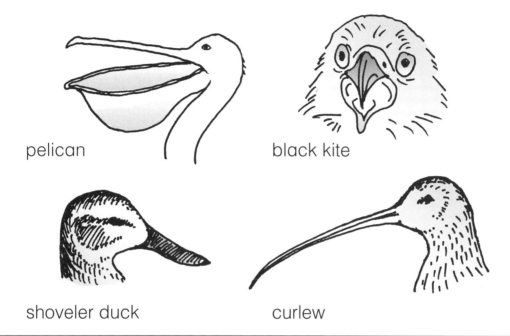

pelican

black kite

shoveler duck

curlew

Draw lines to match the birds and beak shapes to the food.

4

Q7

Birds and beaks	Food
The shoveler duck uses its beak as a strainer.	animals that live deep in the mud on the seashore
The curlew has a very long beak.	tiny plants and animals from the top of the water
The black kite has a hooked beak.	fish collected from the water
The pelican has a beak with a pouch.	small mammals which need to be killed

5

1

Q8a

1

Q8b

8   Alison is testing dissolving. She has some sand and some sugar. Here are her ideas.

Sugar dissolves quicker if the water is hot.
Sand does not dissolve in water.

a | Why does she think that sand does not dissolve? |

She puts some sand and water in a beaker. Then she stirs it round.

b | Draw on the right hand picture what she sees when she stirs the sand. |

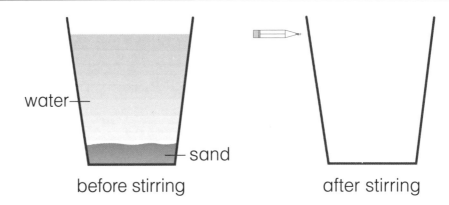

before stirring   after stirring

She tests the sugar using beakers of hot and cold water.

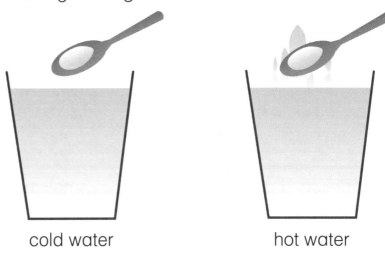

cold water   hot water

c

What should she do to make the test fair? Tick ✓ **two** boxes.

2

Q8c

Use the same amount of sugar. ☐

Do the tests at the same time. ☐

Use water at the same temperature. ☐

Use the same amount of water. ☐

d

How can she tell when the sugar has dissolved?

.1

Q8d

....

Here are Alison's results.

Water	Time for sugar to dissolve
cold	30 seconds
hot	10 seconds

e

Was she right about hot and cold water?

1

Q8e

....

f

Write down how you can tell.

1

Q8f

....

Letts

9   Gavin made a shadow clock and put it outside in a sunny place.

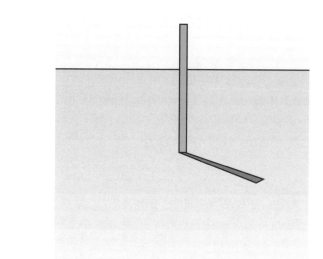

The picture shows the shadow he saw at 8 o'clock in the morning.

a   Draw the shadow he would see at noon. Label it with a letter **A**.

2
Q9a

b   Draw the shadow he would see at 4 o'clock in the afternoon. Label it with a letter **B**.

1
Q9b

c   What causes the length of the shadow to change?

1
Q9c

....

10   The picture shows
a playground.

The table below shows the objects in the playground and the materials they are made of.

Complete the table by choosing the best words from the list.

4

Q10

| bench | steel | light and bendy |
| litter bin | plastic | soft to land on |

Object	Material used to make it	Reason why this material was used
seat for the swing		easy to mould
floor covering	rubber	
	wood	easy to cut and fix together
frame for the swing		hard and strong

11 Kavita went to look at a rock pool.

Kavita watched as an anemone caught a shrimp in its tentacles.

a
> Choose words from the list to complete the sentences about feeding.

carnivore	**herbivore**	**limpet**
omnivore	**predator**	**shrimp**

1 The anemone eats meat which makes it a ....

2 It has to catch its food so it is a ....

3 In the pool, the anemone's prey was the.. .

The shrimp is a herbivore.

b
What does the shrimp feed on?

3
Q11a

1
Q11b

12   The words below show how some plants and animals are linked together in a food chain.

leaves ⟶ caterpillar ⟶ sparrow ⟶ hawk

a

| Fill in the missing link in each of these food chains. |

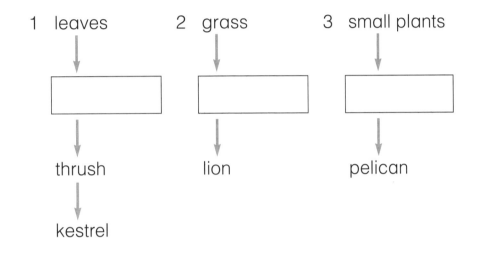

1 leaves   2 grass   3 small plants

thrush   lion   pelican

kestrel

b

| What do you notice about the start of each food chain? |

....

c

| Where do plants get their energy from? |

....

Letts

13 Ramesh and Scott are using a plastic drainpipe to find out how far a tennis ball travels. When they take the pencil out, the ball rolls down the pipe and moves along the ground. They measure how far the ball travels.

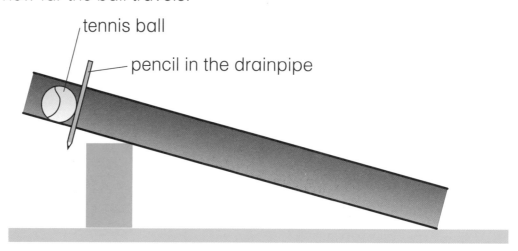

tennis ball

pencil in the drainpipe

They did this on four different surfaces:

the **wooden floor** of the hall   the **carpet** in the corridor
the **concrete** in the playground   the **grass** in the field

a

Fill in the gaps in the table to show the surfaces they used. One has been done for you.

3

Q13a

Distance travelled	Surface
625 cm	
960 cm	concrete
250 cm	
1160 cm	

b

What type of surface does the ball travel furthest on?

1

Q13b

....

c
Without changing the equipment they use, how could Ramesh and Scott make the ball roll more than 960 cm on the concrete?

14 Read the sentences about some different materials, then use the information to help you answer the questions.

Chod, ruck and pash are three new materials that have been discovered. Chod and ruck are hard to the touch but only chod is shiny like gold and it can conduct electricity. Ruck can easily be crushed to form a powder. Pash is pink and can be poured like water.

a
Name the material that is a liquid.

b
How can you tell that this material is a liquid?

c
Name the material that is a metal.

d
How can you tell that this material is a metal?

15   Mary has made a working model of a traffic light. The lights are turned on and off with the switches at the bottom.

The circuit looks like this:

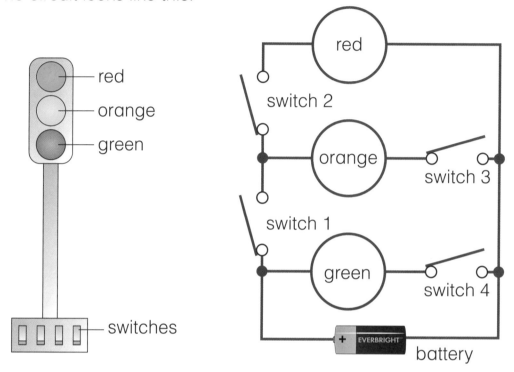

4
Q15

Fill in the table.

What Mary does	Which bulbs light?
a closes switch 1	
b closes switch 4	
c closes switch 1 and switch 2	
d closes switch 1, switch 2 and switch 3	

16   At 12 o'clock on the first day of his **Christmas** holiday, Ross saw the Sun from his bedroom window. He used very dark glasses to look at the Sun. The picture shows what he saw.

a   Draw lines and arrows on the picture to show how the Sun moves during the day.

2
Q16a

b   Draw a circle to show where the Sun is at 12 o'clock on the first day of his **summer** holiday.

2
Q16b

c   How does the length of a shadow change during the morning and afternoon?

2
Q16c

17 Liam is trying to find out the best way to stop ice cubes from melting.

He wraps them in different materials and times how long it takes each one to melt.

Here are his results.

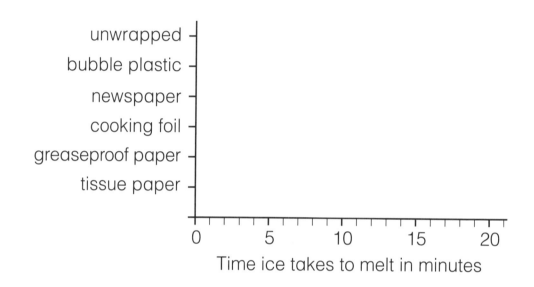

Time ice takes to melt in minutes

a

1
Q17a

How long did it take the cube wrapped in newspaper to melt?

✏ ....

b

1
Q17b

Which is the best material to use?

✏ ....

c

3
Q17c

What **three** things should Liam do to make sure that he carried out a fair test?

✏ 1 ....

2 ....

3 ....

18   Roy and Reena are making shadow pictures using a torch and some cut-outs.

Roy

Reena

torch

cut-out of cat

a   Draw on the diagram to show how the cat's shadow is formed on the wall.

2

Q18a

b   Write down **one** difference between the cat and its shadow.

1

Q18b

Letts

19 Ruth and Philip are finding out about the best conditions for germinating seeds. They decide to investigate temperature.

They put some cress seeds on some moist cotton wool in some dishes. They put one dish in the fridge, one on top of a radiator and one in a cupboard.

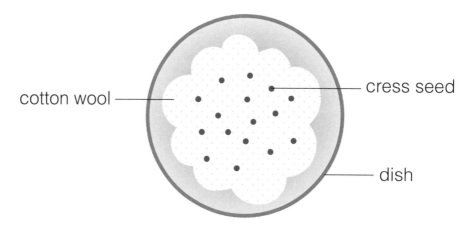

cotton wool

cress seed

dish

2

Q19a

a

Write down **two** things they should do to make sure the test is fair.

1 ....

2 ....

After a week they examine the dishes. Here are their results.

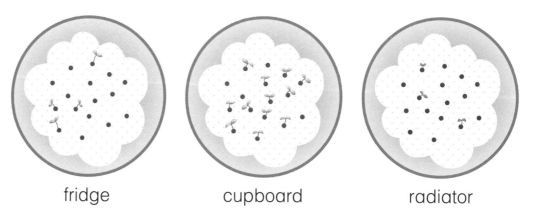

fridge

cupboard

radiator

b | Draw a bar chart on the grid below to show how many seeds germinated in each dish.

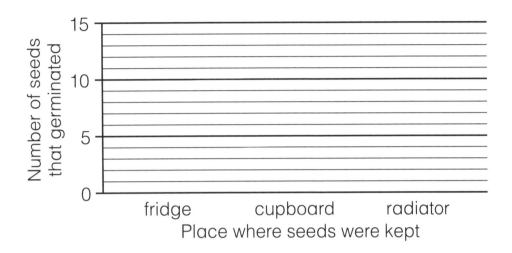

The seedlings that germinated on the radiator were shrivelled up.

c | How could this have happened?

....

d | Here are four ways of summing up what Ruth and Philip found. Tick ✓ the best reason.

Seeds germinate best in the warmest place. ☐

Seeds germinate best in the dark. ☐

Seeds germinate best in the coldest place. ☐

Seeds germinate best where it is warm but not hot. ☐

MARKS

20 Emily is testing different felt tip pens. She puts a small spot of each ink near the bottom of a sheet of blotting paper. She puts the bottom of the blotting paper into water and lets the water soak up the paper.

Here are her results.

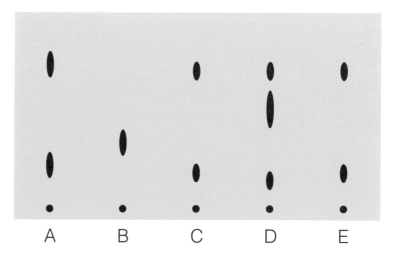

A   B   C   D   E

1

Q20a

a   Which ink is a pure substance?

....

1

Q20b

b   Which ink is made from three different colours?

....

1

Q20c

c   Which **two** inks are from the same felt tip pen?

....

Emily tries the ink from a permanent marker pen but it does not spread out.

1

Q20d

d   Why does the ink from the marker pen not spread out?

....

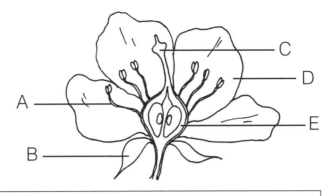

21   The picture shows some parts of a flower labelled A, B, C, D and E.

a

In the table, write the correct letter next to the name of the plant part.

Plant part	Letter
petal	
stamen	
stigma	
sepal	
ovary	

The table below show the job of each plant part.

b   Write the letter of the correct plant part next to its job.

Job	Letter
makes and stores pollen	
gives a sticky surface for pollen to land on	
attracts insects	
protects the flower bud	
makes the seeds	

22   The picture shows some organs in the body.

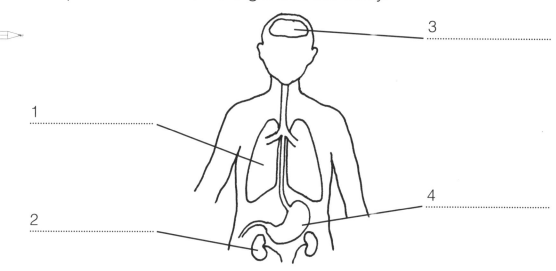

3 ....

1 ....

2 ....

4 ....

4
Q22a

1
Q22b

4
Q22c

a
Use the words in the list to label the picture.

brain   kidney   lung   stomach

b
On the picture, draw an **X** to show where the heart should be.

Each of the organs has a job to do.

c
Draw a line from the organ to the job it does. The first one has been done for you.

Organ	Job
brain	filters the blood
heart	digests food
kidney	controls the body's actions
lung	pumps blood around the body
stomach	exchanges gases

Letts

23   The picture shows a way of getting drinking water in the desert.

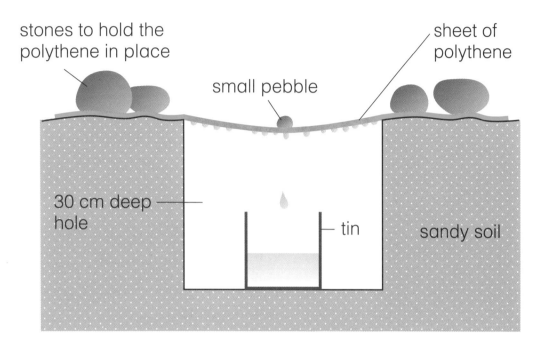

stones to hold the polythene in place

sheet of polythene

small pebble

30 cm deep hole

tin

sandy soil

Choose words from the list to fill in the gaps.

pure   vapour   condenses   evaporates   boil   distilled

1   Water in the sand .... and forms water

.... in the hole.

2   This then .... on the bottom of the

polythene and drops of water collect in the tin.

3   This water is .... because it has been

....

5

Q23

Letts

24   Timothy was playing with different mixtures on the beach.

Mixture **A**
sand and pebbles

Mixture **B**
sand and water

Mixture **C**
salt and water

Timothy had separated mixtures before. He used the three ways shown below.

3

Q24a

a

Choose the type of separation you would use for each of the mixtures. Write **A**, **B** or **C** under the correct type of separation.

1 filtering

 Mixture ....

2 evaporating

Mixture ....

3 sieving

Mixture ....

Timothy then collected a bucket full of sea water. The sea water contained sand, salt and water.

b

> Complete the sentences to describe how Timothy could separate the sand and salt from the sea water. Choose words from the list.

4

Q24b

condense	evaporate	filter	salt
sand	sieve	water	

First .... the sea water. The .... will stay in the filter paper and the salt water will pass through. Then

.... the salt water to leave the ....

in the dish.

Letts

25   Sharon has made a model of the Earth and the Sun, using a football and a tennis ball.

Earth

Sun

2

Q25a

a   How can she use her model to show her friend:

How the Earth moves in a year?

    ....

What causes day and night?

    ....

1

Q25b

b   Which would be the best thing to add to her model to represent the Moon? Underline your choice.

    tennis ball   football   orange   table tennis ball

1

Q25c

c   Draw on the picture where she should place the Moon.

26   The diagram shows the main stages in the life cycle of a human being.

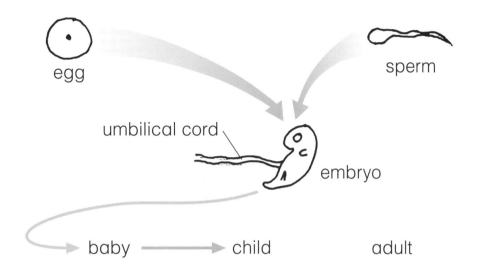

The egg and sperm come from the parents of the baby.

a
| Which parent gives the sperm? |

1

Q26a

....

The embryo grows inside the mother.

b
| In which part of the mother does the embryo grow? |

1

Q26b

....

When the baby is born the umbilical cord is cut.

c
| Explain why the baby needs an umbilical cord when it is inside the mother. |

1

Q26c

....

....

27 Mischa has made a circuit with two bulbs, three batteries and four switches.

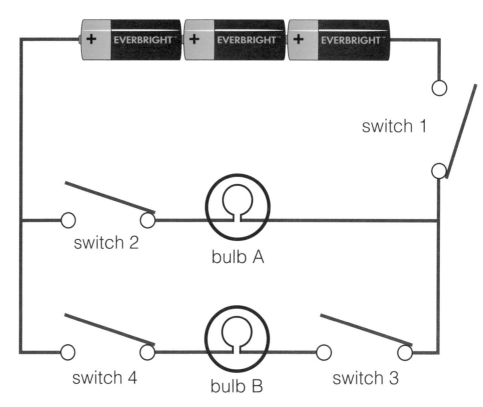

a What will happen if Mischa:

closes switches 1 and 2?

....

closes switches 3 and 4?

....

b Which switches have to be closed for both bulbs to light?

....

28   Jim set up this simple circuit:

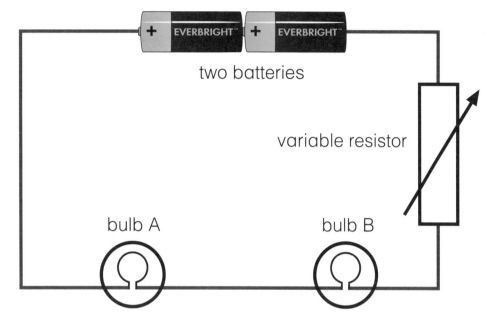

When Jim moves the slider on the variable resistor, the bulbs go dim.

a

| Why do the bulbs go dim? |

1

Q28a

He moves the slider back again to make the bulbs bright.

b

| Why do the bulbs get brighter? |

1

Q28b

c

| What will happen if Jim turns one of the batteries round? |

1

Q28c

Letts

29 Sarbjit used a battery and a bulb like this.

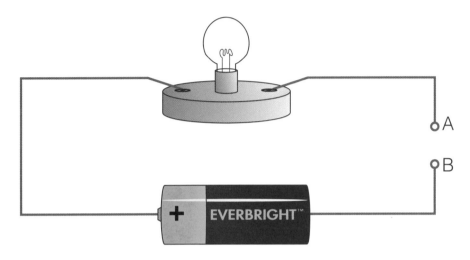

Sarbjit put different substances between A and B.

a Which substances make the bulb light up? Put a tick ✓ in the right box for each substance.

Substance	Bulb lights up	Bulb does not light up
a matchstick		
an iron nail		
a piece of cooking foil		
a plastic spoon		
a penknife blade		
a straw		
a 10p coin		
a piece of cardboard		

b

Which word from the list describes materials that conduct electricity? <u>Underline</u> your choice.

1
Q29b

**gases   liquids   magnets   metals
plastics   shiny   solids**

Mercury is a liquid. It is shiny and conducts electricity.

c

Is mercury a metal? Write down the reason why.

1
Q29c

....

30   The picture shows a plane flying in the air. There are four forces shown on it. They are labelled A, B, C and D.

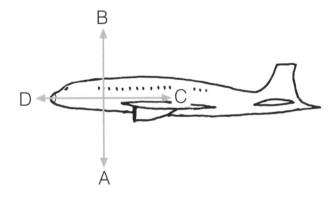

Using the labels **A**, **B**, **C** and **D**, which force:

3
Q30

a   is the pull of the Earth on the plane?

....

b   is the driving force?

....

c   is caused by air resistance?

....

31 The pie chart shows how many plants grow on the forest floor in two different woods.

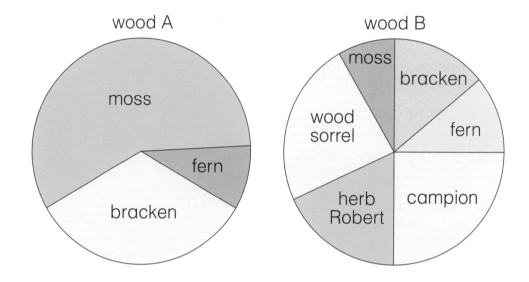

wood A

wood B

a

Which wood had a floor covering that is mostly moss?

....

b

Which wood had the most different types of plant?

....

Campion likes to grow where there is a lot of light.

c

Suggest why campion was not found in wood A.

....

d

Does bracken need as much light as campion? Explain your answer.

....

....

32 Kerry is watching the start of a cycle race. She is at the back of the crowd. She uses a periscope to help her see better.

starter with pistol

mirror

periscope

crowds

mirror

Kerry

a | Draw lines and arrows on the picture to show how Kerry sees the start through the periscope.

2

Q32a

Kerry sees the smoke from the starting pistol before she hears the "bang".

b | Why is this?

1

Q32b

....

....

33 Roya and Edward are testing how long it takes for plasticine shapes to fall through wallpaper paste.

They decide to change the depth of the paste and time how long it takes for the plasticine to fall.

plasticine

wallpaper paste

a

> Apart from the depth of the paste, what else could change the time it takes for the plasticine to fall? Write down **two** things.

1 ....

2 ....

Roya thinks that it will take longer for the plasticine to fall through the deep paste.

Edward thinks it will take longer for plasticine to fall through shallow paste.

b

> Who do you think is right? Write down the reason why.

....

....

Here are their results.

Depth of paste in centimetres	Time for plasticine to fall in seconds
10	1.0
20	1.7
30	2.1
40	2.4
50	2.6
60	2.8

c What do they use to measure the times?

1

Q33c

d Why did they find it difficult to measure the time it took for the plasticine to drop 10 cm?

1

Q33d

e What could they have done to make their results more reliable?

1

Q33e

Letts

MARKS

4

Q33f

1

Q33g

2

Q33h

f Use the grid to draw a line graph of their results. Draw the best curve on the graph.

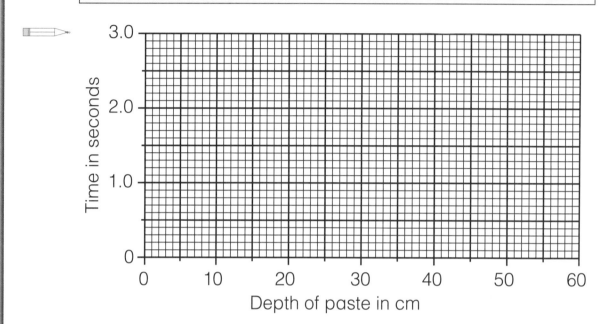

g Use the graph to find out how deep the paste should be for the plasticine to take 2.5 seconds to fall.

....

h Who was right about how long the plasticine would take to fall? Explain how you can tell from the graph.

....

....

- When marking your child's questions, remember that the answers given here are the answers the question-setter expects. You must look at your child's answers and judge whether they deserve credit.

- At this age, your child's spelling may show a number of errors. Do not mark any answer wrong because the words are misspelt. Read the word aloud and, if it sounds correct, award the mark. For example, 'ekwul' would be acceptable for 'equal'.

- When you go through the questions with your child, try to be positive. Look for good things that have been done in addition to showing where errors have been made.

- Enter your child's marks on the grid on page 46, and then refer to the table below to determine your child's level.

Progress Chart

Total marks scored	Progress made	Suggested action
25 or below	Your child has acquired some of the knowledge, understanding and skills associated with work at Level 3.	Identify areas of weakness from the first part of the test. Encourage your child to make a study of living things, investigate the properties of everyday materials and construct simple circuits.
26–50	Your child is confident with Level 3 work and is beginning to show achievement at Level 4.	Encourage your child to try to explain everyday events such as why things start or stop moving, and to be able to locate organs of the body and describe their functions.
51–75	Your child is showing the majority of skills, and a level of understanding associated with work at Level 4.	Your child could make a display of the major organs of flowering plants. Encourage your child to recognise and describe properties that distinguish metals from non-metals.
76–119	Your child is accomplished at work associated with Level 4 and is starting to grasp Level 5 ideas.	Your child could use chromatography to separate mixtures of dyes, such as food colouring or ink. He or she should be developing scientific models, such as charge flowing in a circuit.
120 and above	Your child is displaying all the aspects of achievement at Level 5.	An excellent score. Encourage your child to use a library or CD-ROM to learn about how matter is made up of particles and the process of photosynthesis.

- A child at the end of Year 6 (10–11 year olds) should be, of the above statements, at about the third statement.

1 Lines joining:

glass to windows to transparent	*1 mark*
iron to nails to hard	*1 mark*
silver to medals to shiny	*1 mark*
wood to raft to floats on water	*1 mark*

Note to Parent

This question assesses whether or not your child can think about materials in terms of their basic properties and associated uses.

Total 4 marks

2 a 'twang' the rubber band   *1 mark*
   b 'twang' the rubber band harder *or* further   *1 mark*
Total 2 marks

3 a help you to stand upright *or* stiffen the body   *1 mark*
   b they move parts of the body   *1 mark*
   c Any two joints labelled, for example:
     elbow, knee, ankle, shoulder, hip   *1 mark*
   d knee, elbow, hip   *1 mark each*
   e they do not stand up   *1 mark*

Note to Parent

Children often associate muscles with strength, rather than movement. It is worthwhile emphasising that muscles pull parts of the body when they contract.

Total 7 marks

4

Bulb	Lights	Does not light
A		✓
B		✓
C	✓	
D	✓	

Award one mark for each correct tick   *4 marks*

Note to Parent

Children learn by playing with batteries, bulbs and wire that a complete circuit is needed for a bulb to work.

Total 4 marks

5 a heat it   *1 mark*
   b bending plasticine   *1 mark*
     melting wax   *1 mark*
     drying a towel   *1 mark*

Note to Parent

This question tests as understanding of changes. It gives your child an opportunity to classify changes into those that can or cannot be reversed.

Total 4 marks

6 a B   *1 mark*
   b the Earth's pull (allow gravity)   *1 mark*
   c The arrow on B should be drawn straight down   *1 mark*
   d The arrow on A should be drawn straight up   *1 mark*

Note to Parent

Do not encourage your child to use the word gravity to describe the Earth's pull, as this usually leads to confusion. Forces are exerted by objects on other objects. When describing forces, children should be encouraged to name the objects involved.

Total 4 marks

7 Lines should be drawn from:
   duck to plants and animals from the top of the water   *1 mark*
   curlew to animals that live in mud   *1 mark*
   kite to small mammal   *1 mark*
   pelican to fish   *1 mark*

Note to Parent

The different beaks are examples of ways in which birds are adapted to their environment.

Total 4 marks

8 a For example: the sand on a beach does not dissolve in the sea.
      Award the mark for any other similar answer based on your child's experience   *1 mark*
   b The water should be shaded in to look murky   *1 mark*
   c Use the same amount of sugar.   *1 mark*
      Use the same amount of water.   *1 mark*
   d the water goes clear *or* the sugar disappears   *1 mark*
   e yes   *1 mark*
   f the sugar dissolved in a shorter time in the hot water   *1 mark*

Note to Parent

For part **f**, your child's answer should include a reference to time to gain the mark. This shows that she or he is interpreting data from the test.

Total 7 marks

9 a Shadow A should be drawn vertically down the page;   *1 mark*
      and shorter than the 8 o'clock shadow   *1 mark*
   b Shadow B should be drawn to the left and to the same length as the 8 o'clock shadow   *1 mark*
   c the movement of the Sun across the sky   *1 mark*

Note to Parent

Children enjoy using sticks in the ground to track the Sun's movement across the sky.

Total 4 marks

10

Object	Material	Reason	
seat	plastic	easy to mould	*1 mark*
floor	rubber	soft to land on	*1 mark*
bench	wood	easy to cut	*1 mark*
frame	steel	hard and strong	*1 mark*

Total 4 marks

11 a 1 carnivore   *1 mark*
     2 predator   *1 mark*
     3 shrimp   *1 mark*
  b plants *or* plankton   *1 mark*

Note to Parent

Carnivores only eat meat. Most carnivores have to catch their food, which makes them predators.

Total 4 marks

12 a 1 caterpillar *or* insect *or* worm   *1 mark*
     2 zebra *or* antelope *or* wildebeest   *1 mark*
     3 fish   *1 mark*
  b it is always a plant   *1 mark*
  c the Sun   *1 mark*

Note to Parent

Food chains start with a **producer** which gets its energy from the Sun. Other living things in the chain are called **consumers**.

Total 5 marks

13 a   625 cm carpet   *1 mark*
       250 cm grass   *1 mark*
     1160 cm wooden floor   *1 mark*
  b a smooth one   *1 mark*
  c make the end of the tube higher   *1 mark*
Total 5 marks

14 a pash   *1 mark*
  b because it can be poured   *1 mark*
  c chod   *1 mark*
  d because it is shiny *or* it can conduct electricity   *1 mark*

Note to Parent

In this question, your child needs to use his or her knowledge of the properties of liquids and metals, and the information in the question, to obtain the correct answers.

Total 4 marks

15 a none   *1 mark*
  b green   *1 mark*
  c red   *1 mark*
  d red and orange   *1 mark*

Note to Parent

You can make a simple switch for your child to experiment with at home using a piece of wood, two nails and a removable wire link.

Total 4 marks

16 a An arc should be drawn from the horizon on the left to the horizon on the right *1 mark*
with the arrow pointing from left to right *1 mark*
b The Sun should be drawn in the centre of the drawing *1 mark*
and higher in the sky than the Sun shown *1 mark*
c it gets shorter in the morning *1 mark*
and longer in the afternoon *1 mark*

Note to Parent

Do not allow your child to look directly at the Sun at any time of the year, as this can damage the retina of the eye.

Total 6 marks

17 a 12 minutes *1 mark*
b bubble plastic *1 mark*
c Any three of the following:
same size *or* number of cubes *1 mark*
same place *or* temperature *1 mark*
same number of layers *1 mark*

Note to Parent

Air is a good insulator. Most insulators work by trapping layers or pockets of air.

Total 5 marks

18 a The light should be drawn on the diagram:
travelling in straight lines from the torch round the edge of the cat; *1 mark*
no light should travel through the cat *1 mark*
b the shadow is bigger than the cat *1 mark*

Note to Parent

There are alternative answers to part **b**, such as the shadow is black. Give a mark for such an alternative.

Total 3 marks

19 a Any two from:
use the same amount of water in each dish
use the same number of seeds in each dish
cover the dish on the radiator so that all the dishes are in the dark *2 marks*

Note to Parent

Children at Level 4 should be thinking about fair testing. Often they will say impulsively 'Keep everything the same', without thinking that there is one quantity that needs to be changed in order to do a test.

b The completed bar chart should show that four seeds germinated in the fridge,
12 germinated in the cupboard and three germinated on the radiator.
Award one mark for each correct bar *3 marks*
c the heat from the radiator had dried them up *1 mark*
d Seeds germinate best where it is warm but not too hot. *1 mark*
Total 7 marks

20 a B   *1 mark*
   b D   *1 mark*
   c C and E   *1 mark*
   d it does not dissolve in water or it does not mix with water   *1 mark*

Note to Parent

Experiments like this can easily be done at home to show that most dyes are a mixture of several different colours.

Total 4 marks

21 a petal – D   *1 mark*
     stamen – A   *1 mark*
     stigma – C   *1 mark*
     sepal – B   *1 mark*
     ovary – E   *1 mark*
   b makes pollen – A   *1 mark*
     sticky surface – C   *1 mark*
     attracts insects – D   *1 mark*
     protects the flower bud – B   *1 mark*
     makes the seeds – E   *1 mark*

Note to Parent

Children can learn about the parts of a flower by dissecting flowers using a small pair of scissors and producing a wall display.

Total 10 marks

22 a 1 lung   *1 mark*
     2 kidney   *1 mark*
     3 brain   *1 mark*
     4 stomach   *1 mark*
   b

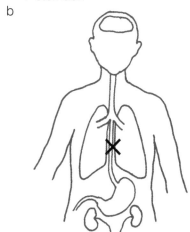

1 mark

Note to Parent

Ask your child to point to where the heart should be then tell her or him to carefully draw an X. Try to encourage your child to draw a small X, because a large X shows the child is unsure of the correct place, but thinks it is somewhere in this area.

c Lines should be drawn from:

   heart to pumps blood   *1 mark*

   kidney to filters the blood   *1 mark*

   lung to exchanges gases   *1 mark*

   stomach to digests food   *1 mark*

Note to Parent

Try to encourage your child to continue his or her line right up to the words. A line drawn so that it stops short of a set of words is misleading and should not gain the mark.

Total 9 marks

23 1 evaporates, vapour   *1 mark each*

    2 condenses   *1 mark*

    3 pure, distilled   *1 mark each*

Note to Parent

Many children confuse the terms evaporate (evaporation) and condense (condensation). This question assesses whether or not your child is clear about the difference. Evaporation is when water turns to water vapour; condensation is when water vapour turns back to water.

Total 5 marks

24 a filtering – mixture B   *1 mark*

      evaporating – mixture C   *1 mark*

      sieving – mixture A   *1 mark*

    b filter   *1 mark*

      sand   *1 mark*

      evaporate   *1 mark*

      salt   *1 mark*

Note to Parent

Sieving and filtering are similar processes. Which one to use depends on the size of the solid particles. Filtering is appropriate when the particles are small, as in a powder such as flour.

Total 7 marks

25 a by moving the tennis ball in a complete circle round the football   *1 mark*

      by spinning the tennis ball round   *1 mark*

    b table tennis ball   *1 mark*

    c The Moon should be drawn close to the Earth.

      Award the mark if it is shown closer to the Earth than it is to the Sun   *1 mark*

Note to Parent

Children often confuse the Earth's spin with its motion around the Sun. Making models like this can help your child's understanding.

Total 4 marks

26 a father — *1 mark*
  b womb *or* uterus — *1 mark*
  c so the baby can get food from the mother — *1 mark*

Note to Parent

In part **b**, womb is an acceptable answer at this level, although uterus is the term used at higher levels. Alternative answers for part **c** include the umbilical cord provides oxygen and takes away carbon dioxide and waste from the embryo.

Total 3 marks

27 a bulb B will light up — *1 mark*
      nothing — *1 mark*
  b all of them — *1 mark*

Total 3 marks

28 a the current is smaller — *1 mark*
  b the current is increased again — *1 mark*
  c the bulbs will go out — *1 mark*

Note to Parent

If your child is working at Level 5, he or she should be developing a model of something moving around a circuit to transfer energy from the source (batteries in this case) to the components.

Total 3 marks

29 a

Substance	Lights up	Does not light up
matchstick		✓
nail	✓	
cooking foil	✓	
plastic spoon		✓
penknife	✓	
straw		✓
10p coin	✓	
cardboard		✓

  Award one mark for each correctly completed column — *2 marks*
  b metals — *1 mark*
  c yes. It conducts electricity — *1 mark*

Total 4 marks

30 a A — *1 mark*
  b D — *1 mark*
  c C — *1 mark*

Total 3 marks

31 a A — *1 mark*
  b B — *1 mark*
  c it could have been too dark for the campion to grow — *1 mark*
  d no, because it can grow in the darker wood — *1 mark*

Note to Parent

In parts **c** and **d** there are other possible answers, but the question should lead your child towards the idea that plants can only grow if they have enough light and that some plants need more light than others.

Total 4 marks

32 a The light should be shown travelling in straight lines   *1 mark*
        and being reflected through 90°C at each mirror   *1 mark*
    b light travels faster than sound   *1 mark*

Note to Parent

A model periscope is easy to make using a cardboard tube and two mirror tiles.

                                                                                        Total 3 marks

33 a the amount *or* weight *or* mass of the plasticine used   *1 mark*
        the shape of the plasticine   *1 mark*
    b Roya   *1 mark*
        it takes longer to travel a greater distance   *1 mark*
    c a stopwatch   *1 mark*
    d the time is very short   *1 mark*
    e they could have taken more than one reading for each distance   *1 mark*
    f

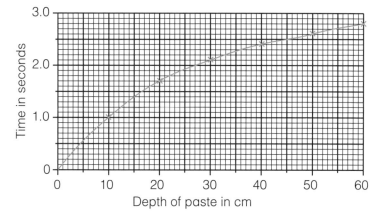

        Award one mark for each two points plotted correctly;   *3 marks*
        and one mark for drawing a smooth curve   *1 mark*
    g 45 cm
        Award the mark for a correct reading from your child's graph   *1 mark*
    h Roya   *1 mark*
        the line keeps rising as the distance increases   *1 mark*

Note to Parent

In part **b**, although children are not expected to be able to calculate speed at Level 5, they should appreciate that it takes a given object longer to travel further. In part **c**, an ordinary watch could not be used to measure time accurately to 0.1 of a second. In part **d**, small quantities are more difficult to measure precisely than larger quantities.

                                                                                       Total 14 marks

MARKING GRID

LEVEL 3   *Pages 1–7*

Question	Marks available	Marks scored
1	4	
2	2	
3	7	
4	4	
5	4	
6	4	
7	4	
8	7	
Total	36	

LEVEL 4   *Pages 8–19*

Question	Marks available	Marks scored
9	4	
10	4	
11	4	
12	5	
13	5	
14	4	
15	4	
16	6	
17	5	
18	3	
19	7	
Total	51	

LEVEL 4/5   *Pages 20–22*

Question	Marks available	Marks scored
20	4	
21	10	
22	9	
Total	23	

LEVEL 5   *Pages 23–36*

Question	Marks available	Marks scored
23	5	
24	7	
25	4	
26	3	
27	3	
28	3	
29	4	
30	3	
31	4	
32	3	
33	14	
Total	53	